F
Shn

The Haunters of Marsh Hall

Can **you** find the secret of the

ghostly guardian?

Allen Sharp

CHILDRENS PRESS INTERNATIONAL
CHICAGO

Published by the Press Syndicate of the University of Cambridge
The Pitt Building, Trumpington Street, Cambridge CB2 1RP
32 East 57th Street, New York, NY 10022, USA
296 Beaconsfield Parade, Middle Park, Melbourne 3206, Australia

First published 1982
Reprinted 1983 (twice)

Printed in Great Britain at the University Press, Cambridge

Library of Congress catalogue card number: 81–10255

British Library cataloguing in publication data
Sharp, Allen
The haunters of Marsh Hall. - (Storytrails)
I. Title   II. Series
823'.914 [J]   PZy
ISBN 0 521 28499 6

Storytrails by Allen Sharp

Invitation to Murder
Terror in the Fourth Dimension
The Evil of Mr Happiness
The Haunters of Marsh Hall
The King's Mission
The Stone of Badda

Reprinted by permission of Cambridge University Press.
North American 1984 edition published by Regensteiner
Publishing Enterprises, Inc.

Drawing by Ian Newsham
Cover photograph by Trevor Clifford

Read
this
first

This book may be like no book that you have read before, because **you** decide the story. It is just like having an adventure in real life. What happens in the book happens to **you**. You decide what to do next and, like a real-life adventure, the end may not always be a happy one. That is up to **you**.

There are plenty of thrills and scares and you will have lots of chances to decide what you would do if you were really caught up in the adventure. If you have ever wondered what it would be like to spend a night in a haunted house, then stop wondering and start reading, following the simple instructions printed below.

How to use your book

The left-hand pages are numbered in the top left-hand corner. Flick the edge of the book through your fingers and you will see that the numbers are easy to find.

You start reading on the page marked 1 and when you come to the end of the opposite page it will tell you where to go next. As you go through the book, there will be times when you have to make a choice about what to do next. As you come to the end of the page you will see what the choice is. You choose what you are going to do by turning to the number of the page shown in brackets beside your choice.

Example 'Did I wait for the taxi (**5**), or did I walk from the station (**9**)?'

If you decide to wait for the taxi, then you will turn to page 5. If you decide to walk, then you will turn to page 9.

This book is better than a real-life adventure because, if you fail the first time, you can try again, as many times as you wish.

To be completely successful on your adventure, you must not only learn the secret of Marsh Hall and find out exactly where it is hidden, but you must also live to tell the tale!

Now turn to page 1 – and happy ghost hunting!

Some British words used in this book:
torch is a flashlight
tap is a faucet
lift is an elevator
'penny-farthing' bicycle is a bicycle with a large front wheel and a small back wheel

1

Mr Crabtree leaned forward, pushed a pair of thick, horn rimmed spectacles further down his nose and looked at me over the top of them. Seated there at his large desk, he looked every inch the lawyer.

'How well did you know your uncle Jasper?' he asked me.

I told him hardly at all. I had met him once when I was a small child. I knew that he had been hurt in a riding accident when he was still a young man and that he could only get about in a wheel chair. I knew that he lived in some big, old house, and that was all.

Crabtree sniffed.

'Well,' he said, 'it seems that your uncle has remembered you better than you remember him. He has left you everything in his will.'

I didn't know what to say. I had never expected my uncle Jasper to leave me anything.

'It isn't a fortune,' said Crabtree. 'There's not a lot of money. There is the house, of course – Marsh Hall. The only thing to do with that is sell it.'

'I think I'd like to see it,' I told him

'You wouldn't,' he replied. 'It's big, it's old, it's gloomy, and it's falling to pieces. Leave the selling to me and I might get you forty thousand for the house and its contents.'

I told him that I would still like to see it. He pushed his spectacles back onto his nose.

'Oh dear!' he said. 'I can see that I shall have to tell you. I'm a lawyer, so it isn't my job to know about ghosts and haunted houses, but I do know about Marsh Hall. Heaven knows why your uncle lived in the place. He couldn't keep servants. The local people won't go near it. I'll tell you – I'm not a nervous man, but I wouldn't spend a night in Marsh Hall. There's only one word to describe Marsh Hall – "evil". Please take my advice, and sell it.'

Do you believe Mr Crabtree, or would you rather make up your own mind about Marsh Hall? If you want to find out for yourself, then turn to page 2.

2

It was beginning to rain as I stepped out of the train onto the platform at Marsh End Station. I still had four miles to go to reach Marsh Hall. I had been told that there would be a taxi, but the road outside the station was empty.

The porter who had taken my ticket was in the booking office and putting on his hat and coat. I asked him about the taxi.

'Couldn't say,' he said, 'not for sure. Most times he comes. Others, he doesn't. Where would you be wanting to go to?'

I told him, Marsh Hall. He stopped fastening his coat and gave me an odd look.

'Nobody doesn't want to go to Marsh Hall,' he said.

I thought that he might be more helpful if I told him that I was the new owner. I explained that my uncle had left the Hall to me in his will.

'Didn't do you no favour then!' was the reply.

I began to think that some of what Crabtree had said about the Hall must be true, but that wasn't going to solve my problem of how to get there.

'If I walk,' I said, 'then which way do I go?'

'That's easy,' he said. 'Just follow the road out of the village. That way, it doesn't go nowhere except across the marsh to the Hall.'

He took down a bunch of keys from a hook on the wall and started moving towards the door.

'Got to lock up now. Last train's gone and station's closed 'till seven in the morning.'

He locked the door and we walked together into the road. The taxi still hadn't arrived.

'If you does decide to walk,' he said, turning up his collar against the rain, 'then don't try no short cuts. If you gets into trouble in the marsh, there won't be nobody to hear you – nobody what's human, that is!'

I had to get to Marsh Hall before dark. The caretaker had the only set of keys and he left the Hall at sunset. I had about an hour. If I waited too long for the taxi, then I might not have time to walk. I wasn't feeling too happy about spending a night in the Hall, but I certainly didn't want to spend the night outside it!

Did I wait for the taxi (5), or did I walk from the station (9)?

3

By the time the taxi had started off again, I could no longer see the light. Soon, the trees began to thin out and I was expecting to see the Hall when, for some reason, we stopped. Without a word, the driver got out, walked a few yards down the road, stopped, turned around and came back. He opened my door and stuck his head in.

'This is far as we go,' he said. 'You can easily walk the rest of the way. You'll see it past the trees.'

'So why can't you drive me there?' I asked.

'Because the bridge is rotten – a few more planks missing since the last time I was here – and if I was you, I wouldn't try walking over it. Stream's not very deep. You'll get your feet wet, but better wet than dead I says!'

I paid him what I'd promised and he lost no time in turning the taxi around and driving off.

He was right about the bridge. I didn't fancy crossing it, even on foot. I could see the water, but not how deep it was. I got out the torch I had brought in my suitcase.

The stream didn't look too bad. The water came up to my knees, and it was cold. Being pretty wet already, this didn't seem to matter. Having got this far, I wasn't going to turn back now.

As I reached the top of the bank on the far side of the stream, I caught my first glimpse of Marsh Hall. There wasn't enough light left in the sky to make out much more than the dark shape, but I could see that it was big – big and ugly.

Crabtree had said that it was built at the time of Henry VIII, but it looked as though all kinds of bits had been added onto it since then. At one corner of the Hall was a tower with a dome on the top of it. It certainly wasn't sixteenth century – more probably Victorian.

I was cold, soaking wet, and it would soon be dark. It wasn't the best time to be standing looking at the house. I would have plenty of time to do that in the daylight (8).

4

Marsh Hall was big – big and ugly. Crabtree had said that it was built at the time of Henry VIII, but it looked as though all kinds of bits had been added onto it since then. At one corner of the Hall was a tower with a dome on the top of it. It certainly wasn't sixteenth century – more probably Victorian.

The main entrance was a stone archway big enough for a carriage and horses. It was closed by two very solid-looking wooden doors, iron studded and with massive hinges. At one side of the archway was an old-fashioned iron bell-pull. I pulled it – several times – and waited. There were still lights in some of the windows and I hoped that meant I had not missed the caretaker.

Minutes later, there were footsteps and the sound of a key being turned in a lock. A small door, just big enough to step through, set in one of the larger doors, was opened.

The caretaker was an elderly man, tall and thin, white-haired and walking with a slight limp. As I was the new owner, I thought that he might have tried to look pleased to see me, but he did answer my questions politely enough. I told him about seeing lights in the wood.

'Will 'o the Wisps,' he said, 'gas that seeps through from the marsh. Many's the fool that's took one for a lantern and followed it into the marsh.'

He shook his head slowly. I didn't tell him that I was almost one of the fools!

By now, we had crossed over a paved court-yard and were entering the house itself. It could have been that I was wet and cold, and glad to be indoors, but my first impression of the place was that it wasn't half as bad as I had expected. Some of the furniture and paintings looked very fine. It was in need of some repair, but a good clean and a lick of paint here and there might have made quite a difference. On first sight, Crabtree's figure of forty thousand pounds sounded to be well short of the mark.

I wondered whether Crabtree's real reason for not wanting me to see the house was because he hoped to get a lot more for it than he was going to tell me (12).

5

The taxi did arrive at last, with black smoke pouring from its exhaust and steam from its radiator. At first the driver refused to take me to Marsh Hall, making some excuse about the bad state of the road. It took a promise of three times his usual fare to make him change his mind.

We set off at an unsteady ten miles an hour. The marsh stretched away on both sides of the road for as far as the eye could see in the rain and gathering darkness. Pools of black water lay in hollows of blacker mud. Tufts of grass and tall reeds looked grey in the fading light. White branches of long-dead trees reached up from the marsh like skeleton hands. It was a nightmare place.

The marsh ended after two or three miles and the road now wound its way through tall pine trees. My eye caught a sudden flash of light amongst the trees. Perhaps it was from the windows of the Hall. It vanished, then appeared again, but in a quite different place. I shouted to the driver to stop.

I could see the light quite plainly now. It was moving through the trees and could be from a torch or a lantern. The caretaker knew that I was coming and he might have come out to meet me. I shouted, 'Hallo! Hallo there!' There was no answer.

With the wind and the rain, perhaps he couldn't hear. I told the taxi driver that I would walk a little way into the wood to see if I could attract the attention of whoever was carrying the light. He said that I could do what I liked so long as I didn't expect him to wait. I reminded him that I was paying three times the usual fare. He said that if I was paying ten times, he still wasn't going to be caught on the marsh road after dark.

I didn't want to miss the caretaker. He might be looking for me. He might be on his way home, or it might not be the caretaker at all.

Marsh Hall was still half a mile away and it was getting very dark. Did I try to find the owner of the light (7), or did I get back into the taxi (3)?

6

I seemed to be coming to the end of the trees and now I could hear a sound very like running water. The road took a sharp bend and, just ahead of me, I could see a wooden bridge where the road crossed a stream.

I could see that the bridge was old and in need of some repair. It never crossed my mind to wonder whether or not it was safe.

I had only taken three steps onto the bridge when I heard the crack of timber. I jumped back and clung to the hand rail, just in time to see the plank in front of me disappear and splash into the water below. I kept hold of the hand rail and edged myself back off the bridge.

I knew that I had to get to the other side. I wasn't going to risk the bridge again. I could see the water down below but it was much too dark to see how deep it was. I got out the torch I had brought in my suitcase.

The stream didn't look too bad. I scrambled down the bank and eased myself into the water.

It came up to my knees, and it was cold. Being pretty wet already, this didn't seem to matter too much. Having come this far, I wasn't going to turn back now.

As I reached the top of the bank on the far side of the stream, I caught my first glimpse of Marsh Hall. There wasn't enough light left in the sky to make out much more than the dark shape, but I could see that it was big – big and ugly.

Crabtree had said that it was built at the time of Henry VIII, but it looked as though all kinds of bits had been added onto it since then. At one corner of the Hall was a tower with a dome on the top of it. It certainly wasn't sixteenth century – more probably Victorian.

I was cold, soaked to the skin and it would very soon be dark. It was not the best time to be standing shivering and looking at the house. I was hoping that I would have plenty of time to do that in the daylight (8).

7

The wood smelled of damp and decay. I could still see the light, and followed it through the trees, shouting as I went. Several times, I lost sight of it, just for a moment, and then it was back again.

Now, I had lost sight of it altogether. I waited, but there was still nothing ahead of me but trees and blackness. There was no point in going on. I turned around in the direction from which I thought I had come, expecting to see some light where the road cut its way through the trees, but it looked black in all directions. I was lost.

I had packed a torch in my suitcase. This seemed to be the moment to get it out. I put the case down on the ground, opened it, found the torch and, having closed the case again, stood up. I must have struck my head on one of the lower branches of the trees. I remember feeling sick and dizzy and dropping down onto my knees. I thought it better to stay there until my head had cleared.

When I did lift my head, I was sure that I could see someone standing a little way off, between the trees. I still wasn't seeing clearly, but it looked like a man. He was strangely dressed in a long, dark cloak and with an odd, flattish cap on his head, of the same colour as the cloak. I couldn't make out the features of the face, except that it was very white. The figure wasn't moving, but one arm was raised as if pointing to the right.

I turned my head in the direction in which it was pointing, but could see nothing. I turned back – and the figure was gone! I felt a dryness in my mouth and a tightening of the throat. I told myself not to be a fool. What I had seen was nothing more than the effect of a blow on the head, together with some trick of the light.

I picked up my case and my torch and stood up. I had no idea which way to start walking, but to prove to myself that I wasn't afraid of 'ghosts' I set off in the direction in which I thought the figure had pointed.

Soon, it began to get a little lighter. The trees were thinning out and I could see patches of light in a darkening sky. I switched off the torch. Through the trees, I could make out the black shape of Marsh Hall (4).

8

The main entrance was a stone archway big enough for a carriage and horses. It was closed by two very solid-looking wooden doors, iron studded and with massive hinges. At one side of the archway was an old-fashioned iron bell-pull. I pulled it – several times – and waited. There were still lights in some of the windows and I hoped that meant I had not missed the caretaker.

Minutes later there were footsteps and the sound of a key being turned in a lock. A small door, just big enough to step through, set in one of the larger doors, was opened.

The caretaker was an elderly man, tall and thin, white-haired and walking with a slight limp. As I was the new owner, I thought that he might have tried to look pleased to see me, but he did answer my questions politely enough. He said that he was sorry about the bridge and that he should have told Mr Crabtree. It had never been very good and my uncle had always talked about getting it repaired, but then he had died and the floods of the last winter had just about finished it off.

I told him about seeing lights in the wood.

'Will 'o the Wisps,' he said, 'gas that seeps through from the marsh. Many's the fool that's took one for a lantern and followed it into the marsh.'

He shook his head slowly. He made me feel glad that I hadn't been one of the fools.

By now, we had crossed over a paved court-yard and were entering the house itself. It could have been that I was wet and cold, and glad to be indoors, but my first impression of the place was that it wasn't half as bad as I had expected. Some of the furniture and paintings looked very fine. It was in need of some repair, but a good clean and a lick of paint here and there might have made quite a difference. On first sight, Crabtree's figure of forty thousand pounds sounded to be well short of the mark.

I wondered whether Crabtree's real reason for not wanting me to see the house was because he hoped to get a lot more for it than he was going to tell me (12).

9

I walked slowly away from the station, hoping that the taxi might still appear. It did not appear and once the station buildings were out of sight, I quickened my pace.

The marsh stretched away on both sides of the road for as far as the eye could see in the rain and gathering darkness. Pools of black water lay in hollows of blacker mud. Tufts of grass and tall reeds looked grey in the fading light. White branches of long-dead trees reached up from the marsh like skeleton hands. It was a nightmare place.

I remembered the porter's warning about not straying off the road. He need not have warned me. Nothing would have made me leave it!

The suitcase that I carried was not large, but it grew heavier with every step. The cold rain stung my face and, time and again, my foot would plunge ankle deep into one of the puddles of water which covered the rough road. Only the dreadful look of the place and the thought of spending a night in it kept me hurrying on.

The marsh ended after two or three miles and

the road now wound its way through tall pine trees. It was just as gloomy, and certainly darker than the marsh, but the trees gave some shelter from the wind and driving rain. My eye caught a sudden flash of light amongst the trees. It could be from the windows of the Hall. It vanished, then appeared again, but in a quite different place. The light was moving through the trees and could be from a torch or lantern. The caretaker knew that I was coming and he might have come out to meet me. I shouted, 'Hallo! Hallo there!' There was no answer.

The wind and rain were making a lot of noise in the trees. Whoever it was might not be able to hear me. I didn't want to miss the caretaker. He might be looking for me. He might be on his way home, or it might not be the caretaker at all.

Marsh Hall must still be half a mile away and it was getting very dark. The porter had said nothing about the wood being dangerous. Did I try to find the owner of the light (7), or keep walking along the road (6)?

10

The kitchens were easy to find. There was one large room with several smaller ones leading off it, though none of them looked to be used. I had been right about the sound. A tap was running into a large earthenware sink which was about half full of water. I turned it off. But I could see that if it had been running since the caretaker had left, the sink would have overflowed long ago.

I had once stayed in an old house where the plumbing did funny things. Sometimes, no water would come out of a tap when it was turned on, then a long time later it would start to run. That was what I wanted to believe had happened now. What happened next was not so easy to explain.

On the wall at the other side of the kitchen was a set of old fashioned bells, the kind used before the days of electricity. Each bell was hung on a spiral spring and each was connected by a wire to a different room in the house. When the wire was pulled in one of the rooms, the bell would ring and, because of the spring, would go on ringing for some time. They were used to summon servants, in the days when houses had servants.

One of the bells was ringing! I went to take a closer look. It couldn't be a draught – all the other bells were quite still. I shone my torch closer to the wooden board on which they were fixed. Beneath the one which was ringing, I could make out the word 'Library'.

I did know where the library was – next to the morning room. If somebody was playing tricks on me, then this might be the moment to catch them. I had only to go back the way I had come to be there in seconds (**24**).

That could, of course, be exactly what they wanted me to do. It would give them time to get away, but there was another way back, I thought. As I had come into the kitchens, I had noticed a narrow staircase, one which would have been used by the servants. I was sure that it must be possible to get to the next floor and then make my way back past my bedroom to the top of the main staircase and the hall. That way, surprise might be on my side (**20**).

11

The house was big and I didn't know my way around it. It might well be safer to stay where I was. I checked the doors and windows. The door to the hall wasn't locked, but the other two were. To be doubly sure, I pulled a piece of heavy furniture across each of them. I turned my chair to face the hall door, put my revolver on the table beside me – and waited.

All this time the lights had been burning steadily. Now they had started to flicker again. The flickering got worse and they began to go dim. They went out!

The logs that I had put on the fire had not yet burned up. I could just see the dim red glow from the hearth. The rest of the room was black. I put my hand out and closed my fingers around the butt of the revolver.

My hands began to sweat and I could feel the hair rising on the back of my neck. I sensed danger. It was a feeling, a feeling that someone, or something, was now in the room beside me!

My finger tightened on the trigger of the gun.

There *was* something – something there in the darkness, something breathing – slow, quiet breathing – getting closer and closer.

'Who's there?' I shouted.

There was a flicker of flame from the fire. I strained my eyes. Nothing! But I could still hear it, louder, closer!

'I have a gun! Whoever you are, make no mistake I'll use it!'

There was a low chuckle of laughter. I fired in the direction of the sound. I fired again. The flashes from the gun lit up the room, but still I could see nothing in the direction I fired. I heard the door to the hall open and bang shut. I had to have some light! Where was my torch?. . . In the bedroom!

I had seen no candles in the room. I knew I had no matches. I had to have that torch. The last thing I wanted to do was to go upstairs in the dark, but now I had no reason to think that I was safe staying where I was (**15**)!

12

I was shown into a room off the hall. The caretaker called it 'the morning room'. A log fire blazed cheerfully in the hearth and a simple cold meal had been laid out on a side table. Anything else I needed, I would find in the kitchens.

I was then shown to a bedroom on the first floor where I could change out of my wet clothes and where I could sleep for the night. With a coal fire in the grate and the sheets turned down on a huge fourposter bed, I was going to be warm and comfortable.

The caretaker mumbled some sort of apology about having to leave and it being late already. He said that his cottage was over the hill and away from the marsh. He said nothing about ghosts. Moments later, I heard the hall door close, footsteps across the courtyard, and the opening and closing of the outer gate. I was alone in Marsh Hall.

Having changed into dry clothes, I felt much better and looked forward to doing some exploring in daylight. I went downstairs and enjoyed my meal in front of the fire. I now had my own ideas about why Crabtree did not want me to visit the place and, so far, I hadn't felt anything 'evil'. The only unusual thing that had happened was that the lights kept flickering. Being in the middle of nowhere, the Hall must have its own electric generator. I knew that they were often unreliable and I wasn't going to worry about it.

An hour passed. Nothing more had happened but, try as I might, I could not shake off an uneasy feeling. I was sure that it was just the idea of being alone in a big empty house. The morning room had three doors. I kept getting the silly idea that something unpleasant was going to come through one of them at any minute!

I remembered that the bedroom had only one door though, the way I was feeling, I didn't see myself going to sleep very easily. I was glad that I had thought to bring a 'friend' with me – an old army revolver which had belonged to my father.

I was going to have to spend the night somewhere. I really had to decide whether it was going to be here, in the morning room (**14**), or upstairs in the bedroom (**19**).

13

The house was big and I didn't know my way around it. For the moment, I could be safer staying where I was. I closed the door again and checked that the windows were locked. The door had no key in it. Since the door was the only way into the room, I turned my chair around to face it, put my revolver on a small table beside me, and waited.

The lights had been burning steadily. Now they had begun to flicker again. The flickering got worse and they began to go dim. They went out!

The coal that I had put on the fire had not burned up and there was only a dim red glow from the hearth. The rest of the room was black. I put out my hand and closed my fingers around the butt of my revolver.

I could feel my hands beginning to sweat and the hair rising on the back of my neck. I could hear breathing – slow, quiet breathing. It was coming from the bed!

I heard the bed creak as something moved on the mattress.

'Who's there!' I shouted.

There was a flicker of flame from the fire, but I could see nothing. The bed curtains were still closed. There was a rustling. I heard the rings of the curtains move. Something was getting out of the bed and coming towards me!

'I have a gun! Stay where you are, or I'll use it!'

There was a sound of slippered feet slithering across the carpet. I fired in the direction of the sound. I fired again. The flashes lit up the room, but there was nothing in front of me. The slithering footsteps turned towards the door. There was a cough. The door was opened and banged shut.

My torch was downstairs in the morning room. I knew that I had no matches. There were candles by the bedside – but I wasn't going near that bed!

I had no fancy for finding my way down the stairs in the dark, especially as whatever had left the bed was somewhere outside. Still, anything out there could hardly be worse than what had been happening in the bedroom (15)!

14

I must have dozed off in the chair. When I woke, the fire had died right down and the room was very cold. I put more logs onto the fire and stood near to it, hoping that it would soon blaze up again.

There was a gentle tinkling sound beside me. I looked down and saw that my hand was resting on a small table on which were arranged a decanter and wine glasses. Thinking that I must be shaking the table, I took my hand away. The tinkling didn't stop. I put my hand out to move one of the glasses where it was touching another. Before I could reach it, there was a loud crack and the glass lay in pieces.

I was sure that I hadn't touched it. I stood just staring, stupidly. As I stared, a second glass snapped at the stem and I felt something sting my cheek. I put my hand to my face. My cheek was bleeding and I pulled from it a tiny splinter of glass. I had begun to look for a handkerchief when a louder, jingling sound, above and behind me, made me look up. The glass chandelier in the centre of the ceiling was bouncing up and down as if someone were shaking it.

It stopped. There was a bang like a pistol shot. I ran to pick my revolver from the table where I had left it. At first I could see nothing to account for the sound – and then I saw it! The huge gilt mirror over the fireplace had cracked from corner to corner!

I stood in the centre of the room with the revolver in my hand, watching the three doors – for whatever might come through them!

Nothing came. Once, I thought that I could hear a sound like something being dragged across the floor in some distant part of the house, but I couldn't be sure. After what seemed a very long time, I went over to the door which led into the hall and opened it. Outside, everything looked quite normal, yet there was a feeling somewhere inside me telling me that whatever it was, it hadn't finished yet! The gun was still in my hand. Did I stay there and wait for 'it' to come to me **(11)**, or did I go hunting for ghosts **(18)**?

15

I thought that I knew the house well enough to find my way to the staircase, once I had reached the door. I was wrong. I should have remembered that things always seem different in the dark.

The first thing that I did find was the corner of a wall. I walked straight into it. I hadn't done myself much harm, but I had dropped my gun. I told myself not to panic. The gun had dropped onto the floor and it must still be there. I got down onto my hands and knees and felt about. To my relief, I felt my fingers close around the cold steel of the barrel.

If the wall that I had walked into was where I thought it was, then the staircase must be to my left. I tried again, this time holding one hand stretched out in front of me. My hand touched something. I guessed what it was and made a grab in the darkness. I was too late. There was a deafening crash of breaking china!

I stood stock still, listening. I could hear my heart thumping in my chest. The house was full of noises – the wind and the rain, the creaking of old timber and, somewhere, an odd squeaking sound like the turning of a rusty wheel.

I pulled myself together. I was picturing a tall, blue and white Chinese vase standing on a table. If that was what I had just broken, then. . . I put my hand out again. Yes! I was touching one of the posts of the staircase. I had only to keep hold of the handrail to know where I was going.

I had got about half way on the staircase when the lights came back on. Whatever happened, I was going to get that torch!

* * * * * * * * * *

Nothing else had happened. I now had my torch and I had my gun. I was standing in the hall wondering what might be the most sensible thing to do next, when I heard a tap running. There should be nothing frightening about a running tap, but it was enough to send a cold shiver down my spine. It was just a tap running, and the sound seemed to be coming from where the caretaker had said that I would find the kitchens – but why had I not heard it before?

I could go to the kitchens and find out (**10**), or I could try to forget it and stay where I was (**24**)!

16

There were only two possibilities. Either Marsh Hall was the most haunted house in England, or someone was trying very hard to scare me off. If it really was haunted, then the best thing I could do was to leave the place the moment it was light enough to see my way back across the marsh. If someone was playing tricks, then I had no chance of finding them by just staying where I was.

I had been going to wait until daylight to do my exploring, but I decided to do it now. It could be no worse than sitting waiting to be scared out of my wits. I knew that the house was built round a courtyard. I had seen something of the part of the house that I was in, but nothing of the rest.

It was on the opposite side of the courtyard that I found what seemed to be the oldest part of the house. The dirt and cobwebs told their own story of years of neglect. I looked into several of the rooms. The dark wood panelling, the timbered ceilings and the great stone fireplaces were still there, but little else. Two rooms had floors missing. A few contained broken furniture, but there was nothing to suggest that anyone had been here for a very long time.

I had been walking in thick dust, but as I turned my torch down to the floor, I saw that the place I was now in had been swept. I tried to picture the outside of the house and decided that I must be somewhere near to the tower. I was wondering why it was swept and what it was used for when my torch lighted on the answer, a lift! I should have asked myself before how my uncle got up and down the stairs in a wheel chair.

I opened the outer doors of the lift and had only partly opened the inner ones when something fell on top of me, knocking me to the ground. I was sure it was a body! I pulled myself from underneath it and examined it with my torch. It was what I had seen in the wheel chair at the top of the stairs, but it wasn't a body! It was a tailor's dummy! I didn't think that ghosts used tailor's dummies.

There were five buttons in the lift marked Basement, Ground, First, Second and Third. I had only to decide whether to try up (22), or down (17).

17

The lift stopped with a slight bump. I opened the inner doors of the lift, expecting to find another pair of wooden doors like the ones on the floor above. Instead, there was a folding metal grill. The cellar was in complete darkness but, by shining the torch through the grill, I could see something of what lay on the other side.

There wasn't too much to see. Opposite the lift was a wall which seemed to be part of a passage running off in two directions. I slid the grill open. It moved easily and silently and the smear of fresh grease that it left on my hand told me that the cellars were used for something.

I left the doors open. I wasn't sure that there was any other way out and I didn't want to find myself stuck down there. Apart from being dark, the cellar was icy cold and had that dank smell of dark, airless places.

I flashed the torch around me. One thing that the cellars had been used for was storing old junk. There were heaps of old bits and pieces lying against the walls of the passage. They had been there a long time, the most modern thing that I could see was a 'penny-farthing' bicycle!

I couldn't see too far down the passage in either direction. The light from the torch seemed to be swallowed in the blackness. I could make out what looked like doorways which must lead to side rooms off the passage.

I looked at the floor to see whether that might give me any clues. Leading from the lift and going off to the right, were two parallel lines. They were wheel marks, and I was sure that I knew what from! It was the wheel chair that had just missed me on the staircase not many minutes before!

There was nothing in the other direction except for a dark stain on the floor. I shone the torch further down the passage. It picked out another stain like the first and another beyond that. It looked very like blood!

Which should I follow, the bloodstains (**23**), or the wheel marks (**27**)?

18

I collected my torch and stuffed it into a pocket. The gun, I kept in my hand. I had hardly started my search when the lights, which had been burning steadily, began to flicker again. The flickering got worse and they began to go dim. They went out!

I was glad that I had brought the torch. I tried to pull it from my pocket, but it was stuck. I pulled harder – too hard! The torch came out of my pocket and shot out of my hand. I heard it fall to the floor. I got down onto my hands and knees and began to feel about. I knew that it could have rolled away.

I hadn't found it. My hands were beginning to sweat and I could feel the hair prickling on the back of my neck. I straightened myself up. I had the feeling that I was being watched – that something was watching me, something out there in the darkness!

I could see nothing. I listened. The house was full of sounds, the wind and the rain, the creaking of old timber, and an odd sound, the kind of regular squeaking that comes from the turning of a rusty wheel. Somewhere, I could also hear a tap running.

I had to find that torch! I started again, crawling around in a wider circle. Just as my fingers closed around it, the lights came on again. I tried the torch. Luckily it was not broken.

With the lights back on, the place wasn't half so frightening. The feeling of being watched had gone, though I could still hear the noises that I had heard in the darkness.

I was standing near to the top of the staircase. The squeaking sound was coming from somewhere down the corridor that led to my bedroom. The running tap must be in the kitchens. It was so loud that I thought it was strange that I hadn't heard it before.

If I was going to do some searching, then I could try finding out what was squeaking (**21**), or I could find the running tap and turn it off (**10**). The caretaker had told me where to find the kitchens.

I didn't have to do either. I could try to forget about the noises and go back to the morning room (**24**).

19

When I got to my bedroom I didn't feel like going to bed and decided to sit for a while in a chair beside the fire. I must have dozed off. When I woke, the fire had died right down and the room was very cold. I put more coal onto the fire and stood near to it, hoping that it would soon blaze up again.

There was a light sound, like the jangling of metal. I looked round to see what it was. The curtains around the fourposter bed were moving, as if someone were drawing them together!

By the time I had reached the bed, they were closed. I pulled back the two curtains on the side of the bed nearest to me, only to find that the moment I let them go, they started moving together again.

I could still hear the jangling sound. I looked up at the wood canopy which covered the bed. I could see the brass rings which held the curtains on the curtain poles around the bed. They were dancing about on the poles as if someone were shaking them.

Suddenly, they stopped. There was a loud crack, like a pistol shot. I had brought my revolver to the bedroom with me. I ran to fetch it from the dressing table. As I picked it up, I saw the reason for the sound. The mirror of the dressing table had cracked, the cracks spreading in all directions from the centre – as if someone had given it a mighty blow!

I moved into the centre of the room with the gun in my hand and watched the door, thinking that something might come through it!

Nothing came. Once, I thought that I could hear banging, like a door swinging in the wind in some distant part of the house, but I couldn't be sure. I went over to the bedroom door and opened it. Outside, in the corridor, everything looked perfectly normal, yet there was a feeling somewhere inside me telling me that whatever it was, it hadn't finished yet! The revolver was still in my hand. Did I stay there and wait for 'it' to come to me (**13**), or did I go hunting for ghosts (**18**)?

20

The stairs had not been used for a long time. Dirt lay thick on the bare wooden treads and my feet left clear prints. Those were not the only marks in the dust. There were clean patches on the edges of some of the stairs and dozens of lines of tiny footprints – rats.

As I took the next step, the edge of the tread crumbled away under my foot. The timber was rotten with woodworm. Now I knew why the staircase wasn't used. There was little doubt that it was dangerous!

I shone my torch up and down the stairs. I had come more than half way. It could be safer to go on than to go back down. If I kept to the side, there might be less chance of the stairs giving under my weight.

There were just six more steps to go. Even though I had been expecting it, I couldn't stop it when it did happen. I felt the tread give under my foot. I tried to grab at the wall, but my leg twisted under me and I was thrown forward. The torch jerked out of my hand and skidded across the landing above me. It was still on, but pointed into a corner, leaving me almost in darkness.

I tried to get up, but my foot was stuck. I moved my position slightly and tried again. As I did so, there was a shrill squeak, followed by another, and another. Something furry ran over my hand. My foot was caught in a rat's nest!

The squeaking and scampering went on and I could feel the rats running over my trapped ankle. I wasn't going to spend the night with rats running over me! I started to tear at the rotten wood to make the hole bigger. Twice, I touched warm fur, but that wasn't going to stop me!

Now, I could move my leg further and twist my foot around. I braced myself against the wall and tried again. My foot came free!

My leg was stiff and sore, but nothing worse. Luckily, I had not been bitten. I picked up the torch. The light caught several pairs of tiny red eyes shining in the darkness, and then they were gone.

There was another flight of stairs, and a door. I hobbled to the door, and opened it (**21**).

21

I was in what looked like a very wide corridor with windows along the whole of one side, windows which must have overlooked the court-yard. I found some light switches and pressed them down. I was standing in a picture gallery.

I hadn't come to look at pictures, but the one which was nearest to me had caught my eye. It was an almost life-size portrait of a young man on a horse. Beneath it was the name 'Jasper Vane Markus'.

As I had truthfully told Crabtree, I could hardly remember my uncle Jasper. The portrait must have been painted before his riding accident and years before I had met him. I wondered whether there was a painting of him as an older man.

I walked slowly along the gallery. I didn't recognise the names and faces, though I supposed that these were past owners of Marsh Hall and their families. There were no other paintings of my uncle, but there was one other portrait which had something about it that made me stop and stare for some minutes.

It was of a man, dressed in a long black robe. There was white lace at the neck and cuffs and he wore a wide, flat cap of black velvet. The painting was yellowed and dark with age, but the face stood out, pale and sad, with grey eyes which had the trick of following you as you moved.

I had spent so much time looking at the pictures that I hadn't looked at anything else in the gallery. There was very little else to see. There were a few bits of furniture and the floor was bare except for a strip of carpet which ran right down the centre. I could see some marks on the floor near the edge of the carpet. They were lines in the dust, as if something being pushed or pulled along the carpet had kept going off the edge. I remembered the squeaking sound. I couldn't hear it now. There was no means of telling what had made the marks.

There was nothing else. At the far end of the gallery there was only the servant's staircase, so all I could do now was to return to the hall (**24**).

22

All this time I had been using my torch. I didn't want that to go out on me. I switched on the light in the lift. I decided to start at the top and work my way down. I pressed the button marked 'Third'.

The lift moved very slowly and, for an old lift, very quietly. The bottom half of the lift was wood panelled, the top half a heavy wire mesh, though all that I could see through it was the brickworl of the lift shaft.

As the lift moved up to the first floor, the brickwork ended and the shaft was made of the same wire mesh as the top half of the lift. That meant that I could now see through it. The first thing that I spotted in the light from the lift was a staircase built around the lift shaft. I could also see both ways for some distance along the first floor corridor. I though that I saw a movement in the shadows.

As the lift moved, the light moved with it. The lift was beginning to move past the first floor. For a split second, I saw it, a face!

I was sure it was a face. If I waited until the lift reached the third floor, then the owner of the face could be a long way off. I pressed the second floor button. The lift stopped.

Whoever was downstairs must have seen me. I didn't think he would still be standing there. I listened for footsteps or some sound that would tell me which way to go.

There was a sound, but not the kind of sound I was listening for. It was very faint and very muffled. It could have been someone shouting, but it was difficult to tell where it was coming from. It sounded loudest near to the lift shaft. It could be on the floor above me, but the sound could be carried up the shaft from almost anywhere.

I was certain that I had seen a man. He had to be somewhere below me and that was one way to go (**28**). I could still hear the shouting, if that's what it was. If I wanted to find out what it was, then the best place to start might be in the opposite direction, on the floor above me (**31**).

23

Some of what I had thought were just doors off the passage were, in fact, other passages. I wasn't too worried about getting lost, since I was still following the trail of blood. I only had to follow it back again and I knew it would take me to the lift.

I had completely lost my sense of direction, but I could see that I must be under one of the oldest parts of the house. There was a white fungus growing on the walls and the stone was beginning to crumble in places. It was getting quite wet underfoot.

The trail that I was following suddenly stopped. There was nothing near me except for a pile of rubbish. I think that I had been expecting to find a body, but there was no body there. There was something else, however – a large and very rusty paint tin. I only had to look at the reddish brown streaks of paint down the side of it to know what I had been following!

After all the terrors of the night, I found myself laughing aloud. I stepped back from the pile of rubbish. As I did so, my foot skidded on one of the wet patches on the floor and I felt myself falling. I grabbed at the wall. My fingers closed tight around one of the bits of rough stone, and then the stone began to move! I landed on the floor with the stone still clutched in my hand.

The torch was in my other hand and pointed at the roof of the passage. It was moving!

I rolled over to the side of the passage and covered my head with my arms. There was a roaring sound and I felt something strike my leg and my side.

In a second, it was over. I didn't think that I was hurt but, for several moments, there was nothing I could do but lie there, coughing and spluttering in the thick cloud of dust. When I did get to my feet, it was to find that a stretch of the passage had completely collapsed. I had been lucky. Where I had been lying, only a part of the roof had come down. In the direction I had come from, the whole passage seemed to be blocked with earth and rubble.

I could either try to clear a way through the rubble (**25**), or go on (**27**).

24

I knew that the library was next to the morning room because, when I had come downstairs after changing out of my wet clothes, I had seen the rows of bookshelves through the open door. The door was no longer open.

I was reaching out to try the doorhandle when a slight sound at the top of the stairs made me turn about. Something was moving in the shadows, moving towards the top of the stairs. At any moment, it would come into the light.

I froze to the spot! Seated in a wheel chair was the small, bent figure of an old man, an old man who I knew was dead!

My mouth was dry, but I managed to speak the name.

'Uncle Jasper?'

The chair had stopped at the top of the stairs. The figure neither spoke nor moved. I found enough of my voice to manage a shout.

'If this is a joke, then I don't find it very funny. I warn you that I'm armed. Now, answer me!'

There was no reply. I was half frightened, half angry. I started up the stairs, gun in hand. I was half way up when the lights failed yet again. I tripped and the gun went off. Before I was properly on my feet, I heard the chair bumping down the stairs towards me. I flung myself against the handrail. I heard it go past, reach the bottom of the stairs, then a crash. It must have hit the wall opposite.

I fumbled for my torch, but the lights came back on. The chair was turned on its side and lying by the library door. There was no old man, either in it or near it. I looked up the stairs. The landing was quite empty – no uncle Jasper, no body, nothing!

My anger had gone. I was just frightened. I was remembering Crabtree's words to me, 'There's only one word to describe Marsh Hall – "evil".'

I walked down the stairs and across the hall to where the chair was lying. One wheel was still spinning slowly, making a slight squeak on each turn.

My hands were shaking. I needed a quiet moment, just to collect my thoughts. I went into the morning room (**16**).

25

It would be easy to go on down the passage. The place was such a maze of passages that I felt certain there must be other ways out apart from the way I had come. What I did know was that it was dangerous and that the quickest way out of the old part of the cellars might well be the way I had come. At least it was worth having a look to see how badly it was blocked.

I scrambled up the rubble until I was near to the roof, and pulled away some of the earth and the larger stones. I couldn't see, but I could get my arm through. I couldn't feel anything on the other side. I pulled away some more of the stones and went on digging until there was enough room to get my head and the torch into the hole. I could see the passage beyond!

It took only a few minutes more to make the hole big enough to crawl through. My digging hadn't brought down any more earth or stones and I thought that it should be fairly safe to get through.

I had had enough of exploring the cellars and

all that I wanted to do was to get back to the lift. That might not be so easy! Now the thick dust had settled on the floor, I had lost my trail of paint! I wasn't going to panic. One passage looked very like another, but I thought that I might be able to remember the bits of junk that I had seen on the way.

I turned a corner and gave myself a fright. I was looking at myself in a large gilt framed mirror. I remembered that because I had done exactly the same thing on my way in! I looked down at the floor – and there was my trail of paint.

It didn't take me too long to get back to the lift. It was still there, just as I had left it. There were still the marks of the wheel chair going off in the opposite direction. I did think about following them but I was also all too well aware that I had nearly been killed following a rusty paint tin! I decided that the time had come to take a look at the upper floors instead (**22**)!

26

I thought that my uncle should be in his bed, but he wanted to hear everything. I told him about some of the things that had happened during the night.

'Crabtree had to scare you off,' my uncle explained. 'Faking my death would be easy, but he had to get you to sell the house. Crabtree believes in the Marsh Hall treasure. He would have bought the house himself and pulled it to pieces to find it.'

I must have looked puzzled.

'Of course,' he said, 'you wouldn't know about the treasure. You see we do have a ghost, a real one, the ghost of Thomas Fulton. When Henry VIII's men were destroying the monasteries, a priest called Thomas Fulton fled with some of the treasure of Tay's Abbey. He was chased and took refuge in this house. The king's men searched the place for days. They even arrested the whole household, but neither Thomas Fulton nor the treasure were found. Some believe that it's still here, guarded by Thomas Fulton's ghost.'

I told my uncle what I had seen in the old part

of the house. He got very excited and insisted that I take him to the exact spot where the figure had vanished. He tapped all around the wood panelling with his knuckles, but it sounded quite solid. I knew that he was hoping to find a secret door.

'Try the carving,' he said. 'Try the carving on the fireplace. See if any of it will move.'

I tried. I was about to give up when the head of a stone cherub twisted in my hand. A panel, big enough to crawl through, had opened in the wall.

Inside was a tiny, narrow room with no window, only a slit of light between the stonework. Crouched in one corner was a human skeleton. A circle of lace, yellow with age, still hung about one wrist. On the floor was a pewter cup and plate. In another corner was a leather sack.

I pulled at the sack. It crumbled, spilling its contents to the floor: cups, plates, candlesticks, all of solid gold, and a gold chalice, beautifully chased and decorated with rubies – the treasure of Thomas Fulton, and the secret of Marsh Hall!

27

The cellars were like a rabbit warren. Now I had lost the marks I had been following and I wasn't at all sure how to get back to the lift. The only thing I was sure of was that someone had been in this part of the cellars quite recently. All the rubbish had been stacked very neatly against the walls, it wasn't possible to tell why. Maybe they had been sorting through the rubbish looking for something, or perhaps they had just wanted to clear a way through to another part of the cellars.

I shone my torch farther down the passage. It looked to have been cleared in the same way for as far as I could see. The beam of light also picked out a pile of boxes. They stood out from the rest of the junk because they looked quite new. I went to take a closer look.

They were stout, cardboard cases, all with the name of the same manufacturer. The rest of the labelling told me nothing except that they had all contained some kind of electronic equipment. The odd thing was that there were about a dozen of them, of different sizes, yet, apart from the lights, I had seen almost nothing electrical in the house, not even a radio.

The fact that the boxes were there and the passage had been cleared suggested that the answer might lie somewhere farther along the passage. I was still thinking about it when a loud clatter made me jump. I swung the torch around, but there was nothing to see. It didn't sound too far away and came from the same direction that I had just come from.

It was the noise of something falling. I could very easily have caught something as I had squeezed past one of the heaps of rubbish, and moved it just enough for it to have toppled over. It was either that, or there was someone else in the cellars.

I needed to make my mind up, whether to go on in the hope of solving the mystery of the empty boxes (**36**), or whether to turn back and find out who or what had caused the clatter (**29**).

28

I stepped outside the lift and closed the doors. It moved off quietly to the floor above. I doubted whether it would fool anybody, but it was worth a try. I tiptoed down the stairs.

The first floor corridor was now empty, as I had expected, but my ear caught the gentle click of a door being closed very carefully. It came from down the stairs.

There was a door at the bottom of the staircase. That was why I had missed the stairs when I first found the lift. I was back on the ground floor, and still I couldn't see anyone. They could have turned left or right. I had an idea. I walked the few yards to where the swept part of the floor ended and the dust began.

The idea paid off! My torch picked out my own footprints in the dust, and another set. I was going the right way.

I followed the footprints back through the old part of the house and had come almost to the end of the wing when something made me stop. It was another one of those odd and not very pleasant feelings that I had felt a few times that night.

I shone the torch back down the corridor. It was empty, but the feeling that someone else was in the corridor behind me remained as strong as ever.

I knew that there were a dozen or more rooms. If anyone was following me, then they could have slipped into any one of them when I stopped, and before I had turned around with my torch. They could still be there.

The footprints that I was following were still clear enough, though their owner could be a long way ahead of me. I could go on (**33**).

I had had so many strange feelings that night that I no longer knew whether they were caused by something real or whether they were all in my imagination. If I really wanted to find out, I would have to go back down the corridor (**37**).

29

A few yards back along the passage was one of the many turnings. I shone the torch down it and picked out a pile of rubbish strewn across the floor. That had been the noise that I'd heard. I was sure that I hadn't been that way myself. If someone else had been there, then they hadn't come my way. They couldn't be walking around in the dark and if they had come in my direction, then I would have seen their light.

I started down the new passage, stopping now and then to see if I could hear anyone but, sheltered from noises like the wind and the rain, the place was completely silent.

I found myself back at the lift. It was still there, doors open, exactly as I had left it. Nobody had left the basement that way. A sudden draught of cold air on my face made me look to the side of the lift. A door was swinging gently in the draught. It was far enough open to see a flight of stairs beyond. I should have realised that where there is a lift, there are usually stairs as well.

I climbed the stairs to the ground floor. The tailor's dummy was still lying on the floor outside the lift doors. I stopped again to listen. This time I could hear something, and not the kind of sound that I was expecting. It was very faint and very muffled. It could have been shouting, but it was very difficult to tell where it might be coming from.

As I moved away from the lift shaft, it got much fainter. I went back and put my ear against the lift doors. Now, it was much louder. I knew that lift shafts could carry sounds from quite a long way off. I also knew that it wasn't coming from the basement; I'd just come from there.

So it was somewhere above me, though I had no means of knowing whether it was on the first, second or third floor. I was deciding that I only had to walk up the stairs to find out, when it stopped. I waited, but I didn't hear it again.

I wanted to explore the tower. I decided to start at the top and work my way down (31).

30

The lift was still on the third floor where I had left it. I walked up the stairs. I could no longer hear what I had thought to be shouting, but the third floor wasn't going to take much searching. There were only three rooms.

The first was a store cupboard, the second an empty room. The third was locked, but the key was in the door. I turned it and pushed the door open.

My heart missed a beat. It was what I had seen at the top of the staircase from the hall, all over again – an old man sitting hunched in a wheel chair!

Before I could say anything, he had spoken.

'Who the devil are you?' The voice was thin, but strong. 'Another of Crabtree's bunch, I suppose!'

I had no doubt who he was – Jasper Vane Markus, my uncle Jasper, and looking very much alive! I told him who I was and, very quickly, what I was doing there.

'Then close the door,' he said, 'and lock it, and don't put your gun away. You might need it. I know that Crabtree plans to do away with me.

Now that his plan's gone wrong, he's got to do away with you as well. Can you shoot that thing?'

I told him I could if I had to. I asked him if there was any other way out of the room apart from the door.

'Not unless you've got wings. Go to the window and take a look for yourself.'

I looked. There was a sheer drop. I couldn't see even a drainpipe. But I could see something else – two figures hurrying away from the house. I could see only that one was taller than the other. I asked my uncle who he thought was in the house.

'Crabtree,' he said, 'and the other one – tall, thin fellow, elderly, and walks with a limp.'

'The caretaker!' I exclaimed.

'Rubbish!' said my uncle. 'Haven't got a caretaker. Used to have a couple, man and wife who looked after me these ten years, 'till Crabtree sent them packing with some cock and bull story!'

I now felt certain that we were not going to see Mr Crabtree or his assistant again and that it was safe to get my uncle downstairs (26).

31

The third floor wasn't going to take much searching. There were only three rooms. The first was a store cupboard, the second an empty room. The third was locked, but the key was in the door. I turned it and pushed the door open.

My heart missed a beat. It was what I had seen at the top of the staircase from the hall, all over again – an old man sitting hunched in a wheel chair!

Before I could say anything, he had spoken.

'Who the devil are you?' The voice was thin but strong. 'Another of Crabtree's bunch, I suppose!'

I had no doubt who he was – Jasper Vane Markus, my uncle Jasper, and looking very much alive! I told him who I was and, very quickly, what I was doing there.

'Then close the door,' he said, 'and lock it, and don't put your gun away. You might need it. I know that Crabtree plans to do away with me. Now that his plan's gone wrong, he's got to do away with you as well. Can you shoot that thing?'

I told him that I could if I had to. I asked him if

there was any other way out of the room apart from the door.

'Not unless you've got wings. Go to the window and take a look for yourself.'

I was going to say that it would be too dark, when I saw that the first streaks of dawn were just appearing in the sky. I looked. There was a sheer drop; I couldn't see even a drainpipe. But I could see something else – two figures hurrying away from the house. I could see only that one was taller than the other. I asked my uncle who he thought was in the house.

'Crabtree,' he said, 'and the other one – tall, thin fellow, elderly, and walks with a limp.'

'The caretaker!' I exclaimed.

'Rubbish!' said my uncle. 'Haven't got a caretaker. Used to have a couple, man and wife who looked after me these ten years, 'till Crabtree sent them packing with some cock and bull story!'

I now felt certain that we were not going to see Mr Crabtree or his assistant again and that it was safe to get my uncle downstairs (**35**).

32

When the porter arrived to open up Marsh End Station at seven o'clock, I was already there. He looked as if he was surprised to see me alive and well.

'Didn't get to the Hall, after all?' he queried. 'Spent the night in the village, did you?'

I told him that I did get to the Hall.

'Spent the night in the Hall then?'

I could see that he was hoping for a few more ghostly tales to add to the collection of village gossip. I was going to disappoint him.

'Yes,' I said. 'I did spend the night in the Hall and I saw as much as I wanted to.'

He could make what he liked of that!

I had already decided to sell the Hall and its contents, though I wasn't going to give the job to Mr Crabtree.

In the end, Marsh Hall fetched more than twice the price that Crabtree had suggested, though not enough to account for all the trouble that had been taken to frighten me away from the place.

I was quite sure that Marsh Hall had a real ghost. I was just as sure that Crabtree had had something to do with a few of the things that had happened to me. Of course, Crabtree denied it, even suggesting that it might have been burglars.

He must have thought that he could make a fortune out of the place, but I couldn't see how. Perhaps Marsh Hall had some secret treasure, known only to Crabtree, and the ghosts!

33

Once I was out of the old part of the house, the dust on the floor was no longer there, and neither were the footprints. I was back in the hall where I'd started and still there was no sign of anyone.

I realised that my search was almost hopeless. I hardly knew the house, but I could see that even I would have no problem in hiding if I wanted to.

There was only one reason for going on. I had seen about half of the house. If I went on and worked my way around the other side, then I would have seen most of it.

I found a way through the kitchens and then came to a dead end. I remembered the archway that I had come through to get into the courtyard. There was no entrance there. If there had been, then we wouldn't have needed to cross the courtyard to get into the house. If there was a way across the archway, then it had to be on the first floor.

I was already beginning to discover that there was no shortage of staircases in the house. I had climbed up and down several of them before I got back to the tower and the lift.

I had seen nothing unusual on the way. This part of the house was in a much better state of repair than the oldest part, but most of the rooms were empty and unused.

I supposed that the lift was still where I had left it. The tailor's dummy was still lying outside the lift doors. I listened again for the noise that I had thought to be shouting, but whatever it was, it had stopped.

I had thought that the shouting might have come from the third floor. With nothing else to do, I decided to take a walk up the stairs and have a look around (31).

34

The spot where the figure had vanished was just to the left of the fireplace. Like the rest of the walls, it was panelled in oak. I tapped the panels with my knuckles. They sounded quite solid.

If there was a secret door, then there had to be some means of opening it, a spring or catch, though it was bound to be well hidden. The fireplace was heavily carved. I tried pushing and turning the bits of carving, but they seemed as solid as the wall. I was about to give up, when I felt the head of a stone cherub move slightly, under my hand. I tried again. It was stiff, but it was turning. I looked at the wall. A panel, big enough to crawl through, had opened in the woodwork.

I shone the torch in. There was a short, narrow passage with a turning at the end which looked as if it continued behind the fireplace. I crawled through the panel.

Behind the fireplace was a tiny room. There was no window, only a slit of light between the stonework. Crouched in a corner was a human skeleton. A few rags of some dark material still hung on it. About one wrist, and yellowed with age, was a circle of lace. On the floor was a pewter cup and plate and, in another corner, a leather sack.

I pulled at the sack. The leather was brittle and tore apart, so that the contents spilled onto the floor. There were cups, plates and candlesticks, from their weight, all solid gold. A gold chalice, beautifully chased, was encrusted with rubies.

I thought it safest to leave the treasure where it was for the moment. I went back down the narrow passage only to find that the panel had closed itself again. The inside of the wood had been lined with stone, which was why it had sounded so solid. I could see the outline of the panel, even get my fingers in the edge, but I couldn't move it. I looked for a catch or spring on this side of the wall, but there was none. My torch was beginning to fail. I could, no longer, fight back the thought in my mind: I had found the secret of Marsh Hall, but would share it with no-one but ghosts!

35

I thought that my uncle should be in his bed, but he wanted to hear everything. I told him about some of the things that had happened during the night.

'Crabtree had to scare you off,' my uncle explained. 'Faking my death would be easy, but he had to get you to sell the house. Crabtree believes in the Marsh Hall treasure. He would have bought the place himself and pulled it to pieces to find it.'

'What treasure?' I asked, looking puzzled.

My uncle laughed.

'Of course,' he said, 'you wouldn't know about the treasure. You see we do have a ghost, a real one, the ghost of Thomas Fulton. When Henry VIII's men were destroying the monasteries, a priest called Thomas Fulton fled with some of the treasure of Tay's Abbey. He was chased and took refuge in this house. The king's men searched the place for days. They even arrested the whole household, but neither Thomas Fulton nor the treasure were ever found. Some, like Crabtree, believe that it's still here, guarded by Thomas Fulton's ghost. You can see him for yourself, not his ghost, his portrait, in the picture gallery upstairs.'

As I had expected, Crabtree was not heard of again. He had not returned to the offices of the London solicitors where he had worked. A few days later, those offices were broken into during the night. All that was taken was some of Crabtree's papers, and a large sum of money from the office safe.

My uncle promised that, one day, Marsh Hall would be mine. One day, I might even find Thomas Fulton's treasure!

Until then, the secret treasure of Marsh Hall remains a secret, known only to Thomas Fulton's ghost.

36

I didn't have to go very much farther. At the end of the passage was a door. It was obviously new, made of heavy timber and with a new lock on it. It was closed, but not locked. I pushed it and it swung slowly open.

I flashed the torch around. It was like several other rooms that I had seen in the cellars, stone walled and stone roofed with no window. The difference was that this one had been cleaned out and, unlike the rest, had an electric light bulb hanging from the roof. There was a switch at the side of the door which I pressed on.

The room was not completely empty. A row of trestle tables had been placed along one wall, and I didn't have to do any more guessing about what had been in the packing cases. The tables were covered, almost from end to end, with electronic equipment. Some of it I didn't recognise, though I could pick out a couple of tape recorders and what looked like several amplifiers.

I had no doubt that this was enough to explain most, if not all, of the 'ghostly' happenings which had been going on. It was then that I heard the door close.

I turned and ran, but it was too late. The door was closed and locked. It was no use shouting. Even if my voice got past the heavy door, it would be lost in the cellars.

I thought of the electronic equipment. If it could be used for producing 'ghosts' all over the house, it might be used to call for help. The caretaker was due back in the morning.

Someone had thought of it before me. The light went out. I still had my torch. I tried the equipment, but it too was dead.

No-one was going to hear me.

37

I walked back down the corridor. I needed only to look at the dust. If anyone had been following me, then there would be more foot-prints.

As I swung the torch down, I saw that there was still a light in front of me. It was spilling from the doorway of one of the rooms. I had put the gun back in my pocket, now I took it out again.

The room was light, yet I could see nothing to light it. There was no electricity, no lamps, no candles. I looked at the windows; they were still black.

It was then that I saw the figure. It was tall and dressed completely in black except for something white at the neck and cuffs. It was standing near to the windows and looking straight at me.

I just stood there. I tried to speak, but the words wouldn't come. I tried to raise my gun, but my arm wouldn't move. I could only watch!

The figure began to move away from the windows and across the room towards the fire-place. It didn't walk, it glided across the floor. At the side of the fireplace, it stopped, turned to look at me once more, then began to fade, almost, it seemed, as if it were dissolving into the wall. The room was empty. The strange light was fading too. The room got darker and darker until there was just the barest glimmer, from a narrow strip of light in the sky beyond the windows. It was dawn.

My jaw relaxed. My arm no longer felt pinned to my side. Whatever else had happened that night, I had just seen a real ghost!

It would soon be light. In daylight, neither the wood nor the marsh could hold any terrors for me, not after a night in Marsh Hall. I could walk straight out of the front door (**32**).

I didn't think that the man I had been following was any ghost, but the place was so big, I might never find him. There was still the shouting that I thought I had heard. I could go back to see what it was (**30**).

As to the ghost, I could take a look at the wall where it had vanished, though I didn't think that what I had seen had been any trick (**34**).